Manufactured for and distributed by Modern Publishing, a division of Unisystems, Inc., New York, New York 10022

2 4 6 8 10 9 7 5 3 1

Modern Publishing
A Division of Unisystems, Inc.
New York, New York 10022
Printed in Italy

Fisher-Price®

Mother Goose Rhymes

Modern Publishing
A Division of Unisystems, Inc.
New York, New York 10022
Series UPC #: 39640

What are little boys made of?
What are little boys made of?
Snips and snails and puppy-dog tails,
That's what little boys are made of.

What are little girls made of?
What are little girls made of?
Sugar and spice and all things nice,
That's what little girls are made of.

London Bridge is falling down,
Falling down, falling down,
London Bridge is falling down,
My fair lady.

Jack and Jill went up the hill
To fetch a pail of water.
Jack fell down and broke his crown,
And Jill came tumbling after.

There was a little girl,
Who had a little curl,
Right in the middle of her forehead.
And when she was good,
She was very, very good,
But when she was bad, she was horrid.

Old King Cole was a merry old soul,
And a merry old soul was he.
He called for his pipe
And he called for his bowl,
And he called for his fiddlers three.

Here we go 'round the mulberry bush,
The mulberry bush, the mulberry bush.
Here we go 'round the mulberry bush
So early in the morning.

This is the way we bake our pies,
Bake our pies, bake our pies.
This is the way we bake our pies
So early in the morning.

This is the way we wash our clothes,
Wash our clothes, wash our clothes.
This is the way we wash our clothes
So early in the morning.

Simple Simon met a pie-man
Going to the fair.
Said Simple Simon to the pie-man,
"Let me taste your wares."
Said the pieman to Simple Simon,
"Show me first your penny."
Said Simple Simon to the pieman,
"Indeed, I have not any."

To market, to market, to buy a fat pig.
Home again, home again, jiggety-jig.
To market, to market, to buy a fat hog.
Home again, home again, jiggety-jog.

Mary, Mary, quite contrary,
How does your garden grow?
With silver bells and cockle-shells,
And pretty maids all in a row.

Little Boy Blue, come blow your horn.
The sheep's in the meadow, the cow's in the corn!
Where is the boy who looks after the sheep?
Under a haystack, fast asleep.

Oh, dear, what can the matter be?
Oh, dear, what can the matter be?
Oh, dear, what can the matter be?
Johnny's so long at the fair.

He promised to buy me a basket of posies,
A garland of lilies, a garland of roses;
He promised to buy me a bonny blue ribbon
To tie up my bonny brown hair.

Hot cross buns,
Hot cross buns,
One-a-penny,
Two-a-penny,
Hot cross buns!

Oh, do you know the muffin man,
The muffin man, the muffin man?
Do you know the muffin man
Who lives in Drury Lane?

Yes, I know the muffin man,
The muffin man, the muffin man,
Yes, I know the muffin man,
Who lives in Drury Lane.

Old Mother Hubbard went to the cupboard
To get her poor dog a bone.
When she got there, the cupboard was bare,
And so the poor dog had none.

She went to the barber's to buy him a wig,
And when she came back, he was dancing a jig.

She went to the baker's to buy him some bread,
And when she came back, the poor dog was dead.

She went to the undertaker's to buy him a coffin,
And when she came back, the dog was laughing.

The dame made a curtsy, the dog made a bow;
The dame said, "Your servant." The dog said, "Bow-wow!"

Star light, star bright,
First star I see tonight,
I wish I may, I wish I might
Have the wish I wish tonight.

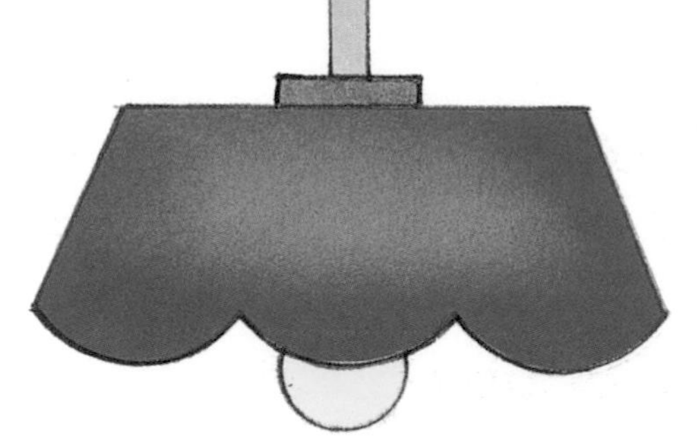

I see the moon and the moon sees me.
The moon sees the one that I want to see.
God bless the moon and God bless me.
God bless the one that I want to see.

Twinkle, twinkle, little star,
How I wonder what you are.
Up above the world so high,
Like a diamond in the sky,
Twinkle, twinkle, little star,
How I wonder what you are.

Bobby Shaftoe went to sea,
Silver buckles at his knee.
He'll come home and marry me,
Pretty Bobby Shaftoe.

Rub-a-dub-dub,
Three men in a tub,
And who do you think they be?
The butcher, the baker,
The candlestick maker,
All set out to sea.

Curly Locks, Curly Locks, wilt thou be mine?
Thou shalt not wash dishes,
Nor yet feed the swine,
But sit on a cushion
And sew a fine seam,
And feed upon strawberries, sugar, and cream.

I do not love thee, Dr. Fell.
The reason why, I cannot tell.
But this I know, and know full well.
I do not love thee, Dr. Fell.

Birds of a feather flock together.
So do pigs and swine.
Rats and mice will have their choice,
And so will I have mine.

The itsy-bitsy spider
Went up the water-spout.
Down came the rain
And washed the spider out.
Up came the sun
And dried out all the rain,
And the itsy-bitsy spider
Went up the spout again.